WWW. Christmas Online.com

A User-Friendly Children's Musical by
Nancy Gordon
and John Chisum

Produced and Arranged by John Chisum
Tracks Sequenced by Jeff Nelson
Engraving and Piano Transcriptions by Mark McClure
Executive Producer: Cherry Tippins

Companion Products Available:

Listening Cassette 0-7673-9259-0

Accompaniment Cassette 0-7673-9257-4
(Side A Split-track; Side B Instruments only)

Accompaniment CD 0-7673-9258-2
(Split-track and Stereo Tracks)

The Dovetailor 0-7673-9049-0
(Contains Teaching Materials, Activities, Posters, etc.)

Instructional/Movement Video 0-7673-9229-9

Cassette Promo Pak 0-7673-9051-2

A division of Genevox

0-7673-3918-5

A Word from the Authors

In Matthew 28, Jesus said, "Go ye into all the world and preach the Gospel . . ." Technology has delivered such power into our hands that with one keystroke we are literally linked to the whole world via telephone modem and desktop computer! What a great opportunity for sharing the Gospel!

www.Christmas Online.com takes us where our feet, as such, cannot go. Ms. Cathy Chino's choir is designing a web site as a Christmas class project. The children are about to leave Christ completely out! CJ and Charissa, through their own journey of rediscovering the true meaning of Christmas, help to bring the good news of Jesus' birth back into their high-tech plans.

Children become acquainted with technology at a much earlier age than ever before. We hope this musical serves to promote the use of technology and all of God's gifts to carry the message of Christ's love for all, to the ends of the earth.

Nancy Gordon
John Chisum

SEQUENCE

Christmastime Online (Overture)

Words and Music by
JOHN CHISUM and NANCY GORDO
Arranged by John Chisu

SCENE ONE

Song: "Christmastime Online Overture"

(The school choir comes bustling into the classroom, as kids are entering from all parts of worship center/ auditorium with books, bags, etc.)*

Kid 1:   I can't wait! We're finding out who made the Christmas Club Web page Committee today!

Kid 2:   Yeah, Miss Mocha Java counted all the votes yesterday!

Kid 1:   Miss Cathy Chino loves her cappuccinos!

Kid 3:   Wonder what's gonna be on the web page?

Kid 4:   *(a boy speaking to a girl)* What is a web page, anyway? A page with spiders on it? *(pulls a spider out of his pocket to scare the girl, she screams and runs)*

Kid 5:   *(putting up Web page Committee poster)* Miss Chino always comes up with the best class projects!

Kid 6:   Today the Web, tomorrow the world!

(Kids laugh but quiet down as the class bell rings and Miss Chino enters with briefcase or backpack and oversized travel mug.)

MISS CHINO: Hi, class! *(sipping sound)* Mmmmmmm! These frappucinos are the best! Are you guys ready to hear who's been chosen to be on the Christmas Club Web page Committee? I've counted all the votes and our new committee will be *(shuffles a few papers)* . . . Mark, Turner, Aly, Cherry, Stuart, Jim and . . . Ceeeee . . . Charissa!

* The sound effect of a classroom bell appears on the Accompaniment CD at 99

(When Miss Chino stumbles on Charissa's name, CJ thinks he's been chosen and leans forward in his seat, but slumps down as Charissa's name is called. Charissa is sitting next to him and is surprised she's been chosen.)

CHARISSA: Gee, CJ, you're the computer whiz. I can't believe they picked me over you . . . sorry.

CJ: It's okay, Charissa. No surprise . . . you're not a nobody like me, and besides, I don't have cheerleader hair like you!

MISS CHINO: I'm sure you'll all have some ingenious and dazzling ideas for our Christmas in cyber-space! Stuart, for those who may be a bit, umm, technologically challenged, why don't you tell us what a web site is?

STUART: First of all, the World Wide Web is a network of millions of computers linked together to create a virtual highway of information. Anyone with a computer can tap into over 184 million locations, called web sites or web pages, to see libraries and museums, shop online, upload or download virtually any information for any subject known to mankind! It's kind of like a giant yellow pages!

MISS CHINO: Right you are, Stu, the perfect way to let those gigabytes do the walking!

CHARISSA: Ooooh, shopping!

MARK: This is gonna be the bomb! My Dad helps me cruise the web on his computer and there's a lot of cool stuff to see! It rules!

ALY: Yeah! We could scan our school photos and put in some hyperlinks to other Christmas web sites!

JIM: We can even upload sound bytes of us singing!

CHERRY: What's a sound byte?

STUART: A sound byte is a byte of sound recorded onto the computer that makes it possible for anyone visiting our web site to hear us sing!

CHERRY: How can you bite sound? You can't even see it!

EVERYONE: CHERRY!!!

(Music begins)

Song: "Christmastime Online"

Christmastime Online

Words and Music by
JOHN CHISUM and NANCY GORDON
Arranged by John Chisum

MISS CHINO: Okay, class, I want you to group up and work on some super-cyberous ideas for our web site. But, right now I want to meet with the Web page Committee. *(To the committee she adds as she begins to briefly exit or move to a small desk with a coffee pot on it.)* Let me top off my java and I'll be right back!

(Kids turn to each other as if in busy work while Committee moves toward the front, centerstage.)

TURNER: Boy, Miss Latte-da doesn't go anywhere without her Giant Gulp coffee cup!

ALY: I don't care if she does have a thing for the bean—she's a way-cool teacher!

STUART: Did you guys know that there are over 25 million people on the web with an estimated 9.4 million kids online every day?

(Miss Chino re-enters with an even larger mug.)

MISS CHINO: Mmmmm! This is some heavenly hazelnut—only decaf for me! As Stuart said, the World Wide Web lets us hook up with resources all over the world . . . from Star Wars to Starbucks!

MARK: My Dad says computers are changing the way we do everything!

JIM: My Mom says computers are dangerous and just full of trash!

STUART: The average desktop monitor and CPU is constructed of approximately 30 pounds of plastic, circuitry boards, glass and wiring and is therefore *unable* to be full of trash!

MARK: Hey! Don't glitch out, Stuart! Dad says computers are just like TV or movies—some people put bad stuff on them and I need to be careful about who I talk to and what I look at online.

MISS CHINO: Great point, Mark! Your Dad's absolutely right and I want you guys to be on the honor code when you're cruising the Web. Never agree to meet anyone you've talked to online and never give out any personal information like your address or phone number!

CHARISSA: Or your Dad's credit card number!

(Everyone laughs)

CHERRY: *me* What's an honor code, Miss Hazelnut?

MISS CHINO: Well, an honor code is making a promise to yourself and keeping it. I want you all to be responsible in all your online activities! Promise?

EVERYONE: Promise!

CHARISSA: I don't know much about computers, but I sure like the shopping part!

ALY: We can go anywhere!

MARK: And do anything!

MISS CHINO: Unlimited possibilities!

STUART: An ocean of opportunities!

TURNER: We're going surfin'!

EVERYONE: Surfin' the net!

(Choir, Committee and Miss Chino pull out all sorts of beach-related items like beach balls, surfboards, boogie boards, snorkels, fins, masks, sunglasses, etc. to really ham it up.)

Song: "Surfin' the 'Net"

Surfin' the 'Net

Words and Music by
JOHN CHISUM and NANCY GORDON
Arranged by John Chisum

(As song ends, Committee, Choir and Miss Chino exit with goodbyes and chatter.)

Song: "Underscore #1"

(Lights come up on Charissa in her room already kneeling beside her bed with her Bible open.)

CHARISSA: Whew! What a day . . . glad to be home . . . Dear God, today was really cool. I'm so happy I made the Web page Committee, but I really feel bad for my friend, CJ. Please help him feel better and to know that You're his friend too . . .

(Lights fade on Charissa and come up on CJ's room, furnished simply with lamp, table with computer, and optional single bed.)

CJ: Hey, Mac, my faithful computer friend . . . I'm back. Just me and you again . . . all alone in my room . . . I didn't make the committee . . . I don't seem to be needed. Oh well, at least you're my friend.

Song: "All I Want for Christmas"

(Lights dim on CJ)

Underscore #1 (All I Want for Christmas)

Music by
JOHN CHISUM and NANCY GORDON
Arranged by John Chisum

Rubato, very relaxed

All I Want For Christmas

Words and Music by
JOHN CHISUM and NANCY GORDON
Arranged by John Chisum

Just for once to feel— I'm in, just to think that I— could win, to be-

Dsus D Gm Gm/F

long and to— be loved— for who I am.—

D.S. al Coda
(repeat verse 1)

Eb2 Csus C7

rit.

Coda

more than just— a face in the crowd,— to be

Coda

Gm7(sus4) F C/D Dm7

more than just___ a face in the crowd,___ more than just___ a face in the crow

Christmas Is (Scene Change, Scene 2)

Music
JOHN CHISUM and NANCY GORDO
Arranged by John Chisu

SCENE TWO

Song: "Christmas Is (Scene Change)"

(As lights come up, it's Monday morning and the Choir is entering, or may already be present in the classroom, with the typical laughing and horseplay, but settle quickly as Miss Chino enters with the familiar coffee mug in hand.)

MISS CHINO: Greetings from Cyber-city! It's a mocha Monday morning and I hope you've all had a marvelous time exploring the Web this weekend! Well, I'm ready to double-click on all your ideas for the web page! Who's ready to download first?

Kid 1: *(raising and waving hand frantically)* We've gotta have the man in the red suit!

Kid 2: *(raising hand and waving frantically)* Presents and cool toys!

Kid 3: *(raising hand and waving frantically)* Yeah, like Intendo and Space Station!

Kid 4: *(using both hands like flashing lights, frantically)* We've gotta have a tree and flashing lights!

 CHERRY: How can you put a tree in a computer?

EVERYONE: CHERRY!!

Kid 7:
(Sarah Francis) *(Sarah Francis, a girl with braided pigtails, glasses and a long list in a high-pitched, whiny voice)* In my research I've concluded that we should have holly and ivy, tinsel and garland, gingerbread houses and dollies so darling, trains and planes and cars that go zoom, bows and boxes all over the room! Silver bells, jingle bells, sleigh bells that ring, these are a few of my favorite things, AND . . .

TURNER: *(Turner interrupts)* Okay, okay, okay! Thank you, Dr. Seuss!

ALY: I can just see it now—red and green all over the screen—this web page is gonna scream!

MISS CHINO: Better than I ever dreamed!

EVERYONE: A rappin', hip-hop Christmas thing!

Song: "Christmas Is . . ."

(Kids come out in vintage looking tree costumes, etc. or pick up simple props like hats, etc.)

Christmas Is

Words and Music by
JOHN CHISUM and NANCY GORDON
Arranged by John Chisum

Steady rap groove ♩ = 88

(Drum cues)

Rap:

Look at me,— I'm the Christ-mas tree,— I've been spruc-ing up— for cen-tur-ies;— No

All sing ("traditional style

Christ-mas page— could be com-plete,— your graph-ics have— to high-light me! O

Christ - mas tree, O Christ - mas tree, how love - ly are your branch - es!

Rap:

Got - ta

take a pause— for San - ta Claus,— 'cuz I'm ev - 'ry-where— in all the malls; Lit - tle

chil - dren sit— up - on my knee, and ev - 'ry-one's— in love with me!

a tempo

(Song ends. Miss Chino and the kids settle down in their seats as the lights dim on choir loft. CJ and Charissa move forward to centerstage.)

CHARISSA: All this is fun, CJ, but I know we're missing something about Christmas.

CJ: What else could there be, Charissa? We've got toys and trees and everything but the whole mall in there!

CHARISSA: I know, but I'm talking about where Christmas really started . . . with Mary and Joseph and the baby Jesus.

CJ: You mean those little baby angels singing in the sky and stars and stuff?

CHARISSA: No, CJ, I mean the real Christmas story—about how God sent Jesus, His only Son to be our Savior and to die on the cross for our sins.

CJ: You think they're gonna care about that more than the stuff they're getting?

CHARISSA: I don't know, CJ, but somehow I've got to tell them that Jesus is really where it all began.

(As Charissa sings, the nativity forms in front of them.)

Song: "Something's Missing"

Something's Missing

Words and Music by
JOHN CHISUM and NANCY GORDON
Arranged by John Chisum

(Song ends and CJ has taken all of this thoughtfully.)

(over music)

CJ: Gee, Charissa, I've never really heard all that before. Something is missing.

(CJ and Charissa exit as lights dim on choir room and nativity.)

Underscore #2 (Help Me Find You)

Music by
JOHN CHISUM and NANCY GORDON
Arranged by John Chisum

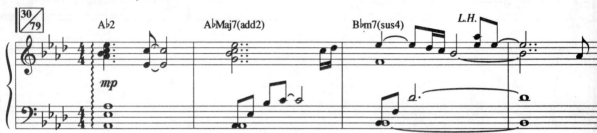

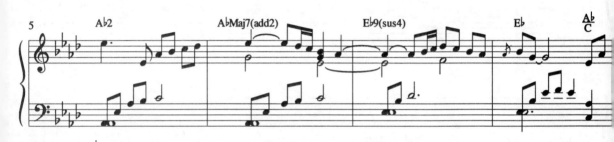

(Lights come up on CJ at his computer once again. CJ is typing commands into his computer and searching the Web.)

CJ: Hmm, I wonder what's on the Web about Jesus and the first Christmas Charissa was talking about. Let's see, Christ . . . Christmas. *(hits key)* Search . . . !

(Charissa is seen in her room again, possibly kneeling in prayer and sings softly.)

Song: "Help Me Find You"

(Lights fade)

Help Me Find You

Words and Music by
JOHN CHISUM and NANCY GORDON
Arranged by John Chisum

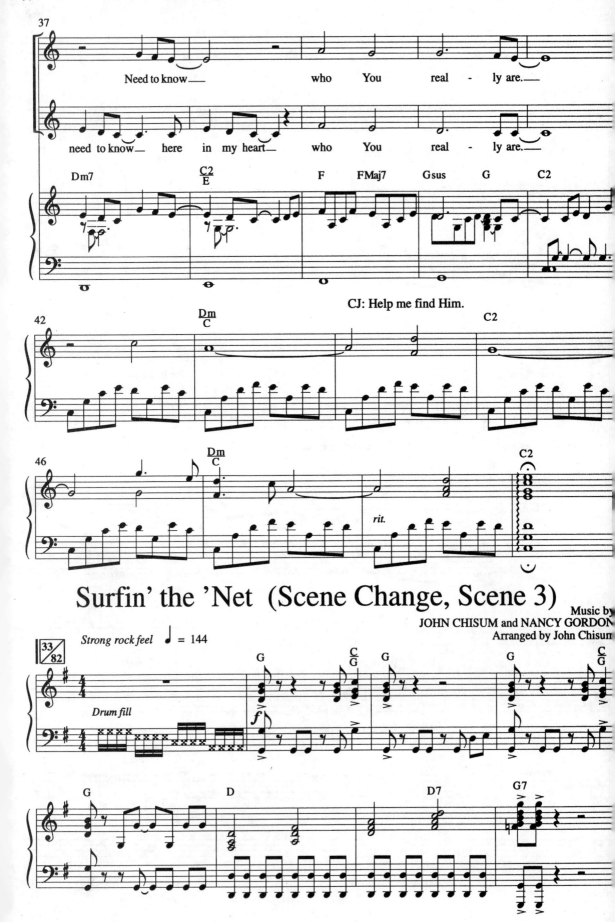

Need to know—— who You real - ly are.——

need to know—— here in my heart—— who You real - ly are.——

CJ: Help me find Him.

Surfin' the 'Net (Scene Change, Scene 3)

Music by
JOHN CHISUM and NANCY GORDON
Arranged by John Chisum

Strong rock feel ♩ = 144

Drum fill

SCENE THREE

Song: "Surfin' the 'Net (Scene Change, Scene 3)"

(With the class already in place, the Christmas Club Web page Committee is ready to report on its recommendations.)

MISS CHINO: Is our Web Page Committee ready to give us an update?

EVERYONE: Yes, Miss Cappuccino!

(Class and Miss Chino laugh.)

ALY: We've decided that since Christmas is mostly about sharing and giving, we'll create a shopping web page with links to all the best shopping sites on the World Wide Web!

JIM: An online mall—Charissa will love that!

(Everyone laughs again.)

STUART: Sociologists have predicted that by the year 2000, billions of dollars of trade will be transacted over the Web.

JIM: It'll be a one-stop-web shop!

MARK: With the click of a mouse, presents come to your house!

ALY: No need to stress, it comes UPS!

CHARISSA: Guys, you know I love to shop, and I love to give gifts at Christmas, but I know that Christmas is so much more than shopping and giving gifts. There's just something missing for me.

CHERRY: What do you mean, Charissa?

CHARISSA: Well, we're just making a big deal out of the wrong stuff.

CJ: I know what she means. *(Everyone looks a little shocked that CJ is speaking up.)* I've been doing some thinking about this, too, and last night I found a lot of stuff on the Web about the real meaning of Christmas. We've got it all mixed up— Christmas isn't about **things**, it's about **Jesus**. We wouldn't have Christmas at all if it weren't for Him.

(Music begins)

Song: "Christmas Is Christmas"

Christmas Is Christmas

JOHN CHISUM and NANCY GORDON
Arranged by John Chisum

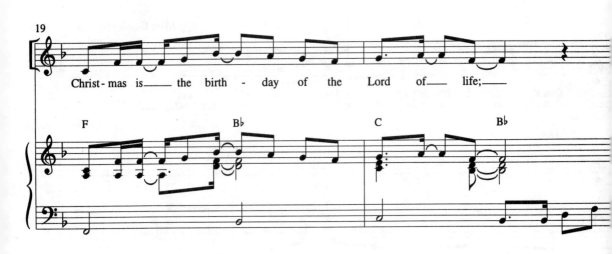

MARK:	Maybe we're going to have to rethink this web page!
CJ:	I've already got some ideas for you guys, if you want them.
	(handing Mark a diskette)
JIM:	Hey! What if we turned the **shopping** thing into a **sharing** thing?
ALY:	And, the **getting** thing into a **giving** thing!
CJ:	Our web page could even become a link for needy children and families to receive help at Christmas!
	(Music begins)
CHARISSA:	We can share the real story of Christmas by giving to those who need to know Christ's love. His love is shown through us!
MISS CHINO:	Bravo, my young NETizens!
CJ:	This way the network is really a net that works!

Song: "A Network of Love"

A Network of Love

Words and Music by
JOHN CHISUM and NANCY GORDON
Arranged by John Chisum

MISS CHINO: Well, you've certainly put a new spin on the old hard drive!

ALY: Let's have a Christmas Club Web page party—we can take toys and presents to kids who may not get anything for Christmas!

JIM: Surf on, sister!

STUART: *(acting like he's surfing)* Slam the curl, dude!

MARK: *(joining in the surfing pantomime)* Doin' the pipeline, man!

EVERYONE: *(doing thumbs up together)* Smooooooooth!

(Music begins)

(During medley kids stack actual gifts they've collected during weeks of rehearsals for children's charities.)

Angel Carol Medley

Arranged by John Chisum

58

Surfin' the 'Net (Reprise)

Words and Music by
JOHN CHISUM and NANCY GORDON
Arranged by John Chisum

(While singing ascending "ahs", kids begin to lift their hands toward the ceiling. The music then stops for dialog.)

CHERRY: How can we go surfing? It's December!

ALL (*Looking at Cherry with hands still halfway raised*): CHER-RY!

(*Kids then hold hands up all the way to finish last phrase.*)

A Network of Love (Reprise)

Words and Music by
JOHN CHISUM and NANCY GORDON
Arranged by John Chisum

Production Notes

It's time to go high tech with **www.Christmas Online.com**!

We're glad you've chosen this musical as part of your Christmas celebration. With a unique blend of musical styles, **www.Christmas Online.com** tells the story of Christ's birth in a way that today's technologically-informed children can relate to quickly and easily.

Designed to involve the maximum number of children with the minimum amount of costuming and props, the setting and production of this musical has been kept simple on purpose. You may choose to go high tech in your production, but those less familiar with computers, rear screen projection and the like should not shy away from performing this work. On the contrary! The entire work could be produced and not show one computer screen!

SET

Where should you perform this musical?
Set in a typical classroom with only two adjoining areas for CJ and Charissa's rooms, your worship center, fellowship hall, or other such "performance" spaces are the perfect areas for this musical.

Due to special lighting needs to indicate scene and set changes, it is not recommended that this musical be performed outdoors without special consideration being given to lighting and sound reinforcements.

Set Ideas:
With this musical being set in the school choir, your choir loft is put to perfect use.

The main characters may be spaced throughout the choir in the beginning. From that point, blocking suggestions are provided throughout the script for entrances/exits.

Although set design may be kept to a basic minimum, you can create a school classroom look through the use of the following items:

- chalkboard/free-standing bulletin board with computer information
- flag
- teacher's desk
- trash can
- pencil sharpener (on teacher's desk or bookcase)
- bookcase with books

Your pulpit area should be cleared of all furniture for easy access by all. Two adjoining areas are necessary to create the space for CJ and Charissa's "rooms."

Depending on the design of your platform, you may need some specially-built "plugs" to create a larger area of level platform space for this performance.

CJ's Room:
- small computer table with computer/keyboard
- twin bed (optional)
- small bedside table with lamp
- chair
- children may contribute items to make it "homey"

Charissa's Room:
- twin bed
- small table with lamp
- children may contribute items to make it "homey"

Computer Center:
- desk or table with a computer facing choir loft

Ms. Chino's Desk:
- apple
- mug warmer

LIGHTING AND SOUND

Lighting needs are divided into three areas:
1) Full lighting of choir loft and center stage
2) Centerstage with choir loft dimmed/blacked out
3) Focused lighting on CJ/Charissa's rooms

The script provides clear instructions for lighting cues.

Sound needs:
Wireless microphones are best for main characters (Ms. Chino, CJ, Charissa), and for as many committee members as possible.

Other characters may speak into mics on stands at various spots onstage.

STAGING SUGGESTIONS

Many staging suggestions have already been included in the script. We suggest you use these as your baseline and then let the natural acting and movement of your choir suggest to you the rest of the staging.

Because the children enter and exit the classroom, be sure to have clearly accessible walkways, stairs and aisles for the children. It is also advisable to have rooms nearby your stage area designated as "green rooms" for time prior to and during performance when the children are not onstage.

COSTUME AND PROP LIST

Because our setting is a classroom, children will dress in their everyday school clothes (jeans, pullover sweaters, polo shirts, khakis, etc). Ms. Chino should wear something a little more outlandish (brightly-colored floral dresses, etc.), to accent her eccentric nature and should be prepared for costume changes between scenes. The children may facilitate costume changes by slipping on or off a sweater, t-shirt, jacket or polo shirt while keeping on the same jeans, slacks, or skirts.

Note: If your church or church school uses uniforms, feel free to use them and have Ms. Chino's uniform a little more eccentric by using cat eyeglasses or funny hairdos.

Other costuming needs:
In the song "Surfin' the Net" and its reprise, Ms. Chino and all the class should have easy access to hidden beach paraphernalia such as beach balls, sunglasses, bottles of tanning lotion, volleyballs, boogie boards, surf boards, paddles and paddle ball games, etc. to ham it up. During the dialogue just before this song, some choir members may actually slip offstage to change into beach costumes such as shorts, flippers, snorkling gear, etc. with supersoaker waterguns without water!

In the song "Christmas Is . . . ," children may be costumed as trees, toys, Santas, reindeer and anything popular with the commercialized version of Christmas. Feel free to add cute pre-schoolers or older adults in this song.

In "Something's Missing," children will enact the nativity and will need costuming for Wisemen, Shepherds, Mary, Joseph, etc. Utilize all ages here, as well, especially if your choir is small. If your choir is large, consider adding live animals for expansion.

The "Angel Carol Medley" provides a great opportunity once again to use your pre-schoolers dressed as angels, etc.

Character	Costumes	Props
Ms. Chino	Three dresses with bright patterns or uniforms	Large coffee mugs, notebook, pencil
Choir	School clothes (jeans, etc) or uniforms	Books, backpacks, notebooks
CJ *(if boy)*	Horn-rimmed glasses	same

CJ *(if girl)*   Very plain hairstyle/glasses

Charissa   Cheerleader look—lots of hair!   same

Stuart   Brainy looking with glasses/preppy clothes

Sarah Francis Braided pig tails/round glasses

Cherry   A typical airheaded look...

Cast of Characters:
The Christmas Club Web Page Committee
Mark
Turner
Stuart
Jim
Cherry
Aly
Charissa

The Christmas Club Web Page Committee is a group of kids who are heading up the school choir project of creating a webpage on the internet to celebrate Christmas.

Ms. Cathy Chino—An avowed coffee lover, Ms. Chino is the school choir director and is never seen without a large coffee mug at hand. The kids never quite get her name right, with everything from "Miss Hazlenut" to "Miss Cappucino."

CJ—A ten to twelve year-old boy more into his computer than anything else.

Charissa—A "together" ten to twelve year-old girl who befriends CJ. She is part of The Christmas Club Web Page Committee.

Choir—All the kids at the school who are rehearsing for the Christmas program.

Other characters/costumes:
Santa and helpers
Reindeer
Elves
Various toys
Mary, Joseph, Jesus
Angels, shepherds, wisemen, etc.